Meg and Mack
sit on the rug.

The picnic

Nat has a picnic on the rug. She has a jug and cups.

Nat has six buns but no bun for a rabbit.

Mack hops off.
He hops to the hut.

Meg runs to the hut
to get Mack.

Mack is not in the hut.
Is he at the log?

Mack has a picnic too.

The picnic

Before reading

Say the sounds: c k ck j qu v w x y z zz ff ll ss
Ensure the children use the pure sounds for the consonants without the added "uh" sound, e.g. "llll" not "luh".

Practise blending the sounds: Meg Mack six jug buns cups rabbit picnic hops hut rug sit runs log Nat bun

High-frequency words: and off get at on not in but
Tricky words: the she too no to is he has for

Vocabulary check: Review meaning of verbs "hop" and "run". Which animals would hop and which animals would run?

Story discussion: Look at the cover illustration and read the title. Talk about what a picnic is. Ask children if they have been on a picnic. What are some of the things you might take with you on a picnic?

Teaching points: Review two-syllable words and how to decode them focusing on one syllable at a time, e.g. pic/nic, lem/on. Introduce two-syllable words that have double letters in the middle, e.g. rab/bit. More words to sound-talk and blend: ten/nis, kit/ten, but/ton, hap/pen, pup/pet, sud/den, par/rot, rib/bon.

After reading

Comprehension:
- Who was Nat having a picnic with?
- What food did she take along?
- Where did Mack hop off to? Why do you think he left Nat and Meg?
- What was Mack doing at the end of the story?

Fluency: Speed read the words again from the inside front cover.